BASICS OF KEYBOARD THEORY

LEVEL V

Fifth Edition

Julie McIntosh Johnson

J. Johnson Music Publications

5062 Siesta Lane
Yorba Linda, CA 92886
Phone: (714) 961-0257
Fax: (714) 242-9350
www.bktmusic.com
info@bktmusic.com

Basics of Keyboard Theory, Level V, Fifth Edition

Published by:

J. Johnson Music Publications
5062 Siesta Ln.
Yorba Linda, CA 92886 U.S.A.
(714) 961-0257

©1997 by Julie McIntosh Johnson. Revised.
Previous editions ©1983, 1991, and 1992, and 1997, Julie McIntosh Johnson.
Printed in United States of America

Library of Congress Cataloging in Publication Data

Johnson, Julie Anne McIntosh
Basics of Keyboard Theory, Level V, Fifth Edition

ISBN 1-891757-05-9 Softcover

LC TX 4-721-493

TO THE TEACHER

Intended as a supplement to private or group music lessons, *Basics of Keyboard Theory, Level V* presents basic theory concepts to the intermediate music student. This level is to be used with the student who has had approximately 5-6 years of music lessons, and is playing piano literature at the level of Clementi's *Sonatina, Op. 36, No. 3*, or Grieg's *Watchman's Song*.

Basics of Keyboard Theory, Level V is divided into 17 lessons, with two reviews, and a test at the end. Application of each theory concept is made to piano music of the level. Lessons may be combined with one another or divided into smaller sections, depending on the ability of the student. Whenever possible, it is helpful to demonstrate theory concepts on the keyboard, and apply them to the music the student is playing.

Learning music theory can be a very rewarding experience for the student when carefully applied to lessons. *Basics of Keyboard Theory, Level V*, is an important part of learning this valuable subject.

BASICS OF KEYBOARD THEORY
COMPUTER ACTIVITIES
by
Nancy Plourde
with
Julie McIntosh Johnson and Anita Yee Belansky

Colorful, exciting games that reinforce Basics of Keyboard Theory lessons!

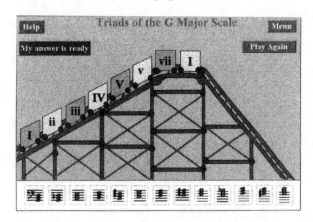

LEVELS PREPARATORY, 1, and 2: 30 GAMES, 10 PER LEVEL!
LEVELS 3 and 4: 20 GAMES, 10 PER LEVEL!
LEVELS 5 and 6: 20 GAMES, 10 PER LEVEL!
Corresponds with MTAC CM Syllabus & *Basics of Keyboard Theory* books, or may be used independently.

Download a free demo at www.pbjmusic.com
---**Order Form**--

Name_____

Address_____

City_____State____Zip_____

Email_____Phone_____

Mail to: PBJ Music Publications
5062 Siesta Ln.
Yorba Linda, CA 92886
(714) 961-0257

Qty		Cost
_____	Levels Prep-II, Mac/PC: $49.95	_____
_____	Levels III-IV, Mac/PC: $39.95	_____
_____	Levels 5-6, PC only: $49.95	_____
	Sub Total:	_____
	Sales Tax (CA, AZ, TX residents)	_____
	Shipping:	$5.00
	Total:	_____

System Requirements
IBM or compatible: 486 33 MHz or higher, Windows 3.1, 95, 98, NT, or XP, 8 MB RAM, 5 MB hard disk space, MIDI Soundcard, VGA monitor.
Macintosh: System 7 or greater, 8 MB RAM, 3 MB hard disk space available, color monitor.

TABLE OF CONTENTS

Basics of Keyboard Theory is dedicated to my husband Rob, without whose love, support, help, and incredible patience, this series would not have been possible.

LESSON 1
MAJOR AND MINOR KEY SIGNATURES

The **KEY SIGNATURE** for a musical composition is found at the beginning of the piece, next to the clef signs.

The **KEY SIGNATURE** tells you two things:

1. The **key** or **tonality** of the music.

2. **Which notes** in the music are to **receive sharps or flats**.

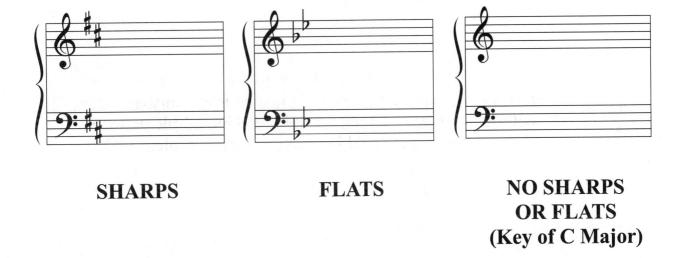

SHARPS   **FLATS**   **NO SHARPS
OR FLATS
(Key of C Major)**

If the key signature has **SHARPS**, they will be written in this order, on these lines and spaces. This is called the **ORDER OF SHARPS.**

FCGDAEB

A saying to help you remember this order is:

Fat Cats Go Down Alleys Eating Bologna

If a key signature has one sharp, it will be F♯. If a key signature has two sharps, they will be F♯ and C♯, etc.

1. Fill in the blanks.

a. If a key signature has two sharps, they will be _____ and _____.

b. If a key signature has three sharps, they will be _____, _____, and _____.

c. If a key signature has one sharp, it will be _____.

d. If a key signature has six sharps, they will be _____, _____, _____,

_____, _____, and _____.

2. Write the ORDER OF SHARPS three times on the staff below, in both clefs.

To find out which Major key a group of sharps represents, find and name the last sharp (the sharp furthest to the right), then go up a half step from that sharp. The note which is a half step above the last sharp is the name of the Major key.

Three sharps: F♯, C♯, G♯

Last sharp is G♯

A half step above G♯ is A

Key of A Major

3. Name these Major keys. (The first one is done for you..)

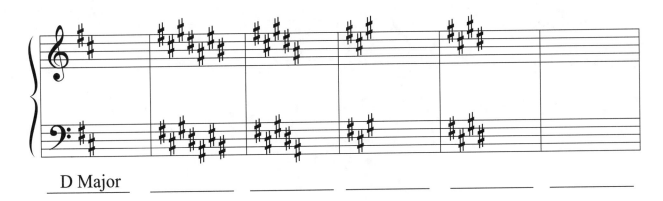

D Major _____ _____ _____ _____ _____

To determine which sharps are in a Major key, find the sharp which is a half step below the name of the key. Name all the sharps from the Order of Sharps up to and including that sharp.

Key of D Major

A half step below D is C♯

Name all sharps, from the Order of Sharps, up to and including C♯

F♯ and C♯

4. Write the key signatures for these keys.

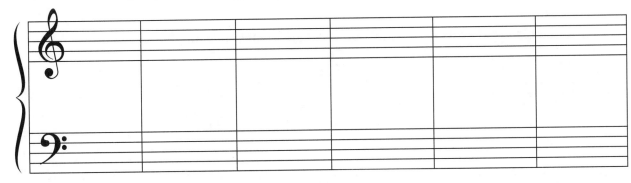

G Major   F♯ Major   A Major   B Major   E Major   C♯ Major

If a key signature has flats, they will be in the following order, written on these lines and spaces. This is called the **ORDER OF FLATS.**

THE ORDER OF FLATS

The Order of Flats can be memorized this way:

BEAD Gum Candy Fruit

If a key signature has one flat, it will be B♭. If it has two flats, they will be B♭ and E♭, etc.

5. Fill in the blanks.

a. If a key signature has two flats, they are _____ and _____.

b. If a key signature has four flats, they are _____, _____, _____, and _____.

c. If a key signature has three flats, they are _____, _____, and _____.

d. If a key signature has five flats, they are _____, _____, _____, _____, and

_____.

6. Write the Order of Flats three times on the staff below, in both clefs.

To determine which Major key a group of flats represents, simply name the next to last flat.

Three flats: B♭, E♭, A♭

Next to last flat is E♭

Key of E♭ Major

The key signature for F Major has to be memorized. It has one flat: B♭.

KEY SIGNATURE FOR F MAJOR

7. Name these Major keys.

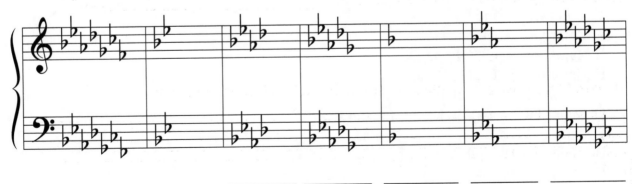

To determine which flats are needed for a given key, name all the flats from the Order of Flats up to and including the name of the key, then add one more.

Key of E♭ Major

Name all flats from the Order of Flats up to and including E♭, then add one more.

B♭, E♭, A♭

8. Write the key signatures for these keys. (The first one is done for you.)

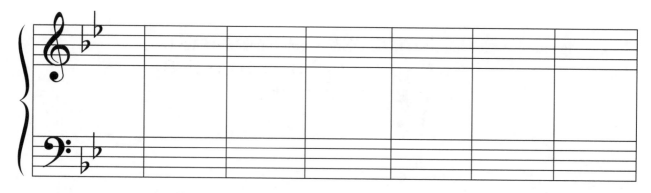

B♭ Major   A♭ Major   D♭ Major   C♭ Major   E♭ Major   F Major   G♭ Major

9. Memorize these key signature.

C Major has no sharps or flats
G Major has F♯
D Major has F♯ and C♯
A Major has F♯, C♯, and G♯
E Major has F♯, C♯, G♯, and D♯
B Major has F♯, C♯, G♯, D♯, and A♯
F♯ Major has F♯, C♯, G♯, D♯, A♯, and E♯
C♯ Major has F♯, C♯, G♯, D♯, A♯, E♯, and B♯
F Major has B♭
B♭ Major has B♭, and E♭
E♭ Major has B♭, E♭, and A♭
A♭ Major has B♭, E♭, A♭, and D♭
D♭ Major has B♭, E♭, A♭, D♭, and G♭
G♭ Major has B♭, E♭, A♭, D♭, G♭, and C♭
C♭ Major has B♭, E♭, A♭, D♭, G♭, C♭, and F♭

Each Major key has a **<u>RELATIVE MINOR.</u>** The relative minor is found by going down three half steps from the name of the Major key.

KEY SIGNATURE FOR D MAJOR
THREE HALF STEPS BELOW D IS B
KEY OF B MINOR

One way to determine whether a composition is in the Major or minor key is to look at the last note of the piece. It is usually the same as the name of the key. (For example, a piece which is in the key of a minor will probably end on A.) Also, look at the music to find the note around which the music appears to be centered; which note appears to be the main note of the piece.

Go Golfing with key signatures and PBJ's
Basics of Keyboard Theory Computer Activities, Levels 5-6.
PBJ Music Publications, 5062 Siesta Ln., Yorba Linda, CA, 92886, 714-961-0257

10. Write the names of the relative minors for the following Major keys. (Determine the relative minor by going <u>down</u> three half steps from the name of the Major key.) The first one is done for you.

    a. G Major   e minor

    b. E♭ Major   _____

    c. C Major   _____

    d. F Major   _____

    e. B♭ Major   _____

    f. D Major   _____

    g. A♭ Major   _____

11. Give the name of the relative Major for each of the following minor keys. (Determine the relative Major by going <u>up</u> three half steps.) The first one is done for you.

    a. d minor   F Major

    b. e minor   _____

    c. f minor   _____

    d. c minor   _____

    e. a minor   _____

    f. g minor   _____

    g. b minor   _____

12. Name these minor keys. (Determine the Major key name, then go down three half steps to find the relative minor.) The first one is done for you.

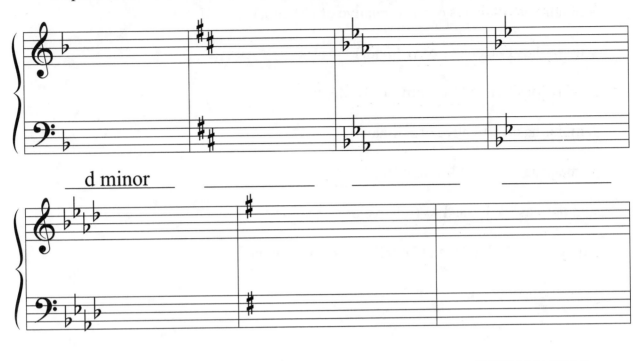

    d minor

13. Write the key signatures for these minor keys. (Go <u>up</u> three half steps to find the relative Major, then write the key signature for that Major key.) The first one is done for you.

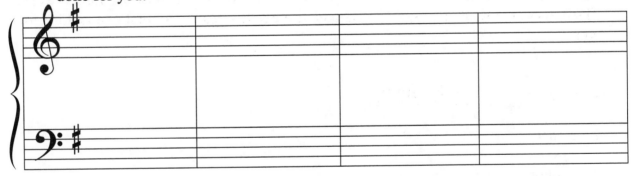

    e minor   c minor   g minor   d minor

    b minor   f minor   a minor

14. Memorize these key signatures.

a minor has no sharps or flats (relative of C Major)

e minor has F♯ (relative of G Major)

b minor has F♯ and C♯ (relative of D Major)

d minor has B♭ (relative of F Major)

g minor has B♭ and E♭ (relative of B♭ Major)

c minor has B♭, E♭, and A♭ (relative of E♭ Major)

f minor has B♭, E♭, A♭, and D♭ (relative of A♭ Major)

LESSON 2
MAJOR AND MINOR SCALES

SCALES have eight notes, which are each a step apart. They begin and end with notes of the same letter name.

MAJOR SCALES contain all the sharps or flats from the Major key signature with the same name.

Example: D Major Scale begins and ends with the note "D," and has F♯ and C♯.

D MAJOR SCALE

There are several forms of minor scales. Two of these are **Natural Minor** and **Harmonic Minor.**

NATURAL MINOR SCALES contain all the sharps or flats from the minor key signature with the same letter name.

Example: d natural minor scale begins and ends with the note "D," and has B♭.

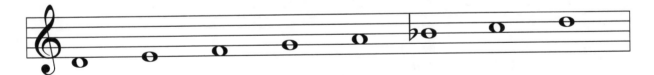

D NATURAL MINOR SCALE

Can you finish the scale before the firecracker explodes? Test your skills with PBJ's *Basics of Keyboard Theory Computer Activities, Levels 5-6.*
www.pbjmusic.com   teachme@pbjmusic.com

HARMONIC MINOR SCALES are created by raising the 7th note of the scale a half step. This creates a half step, rather than a whole step, between the 7th and 8th notes of the scale, making the 7th note a "leading tone."

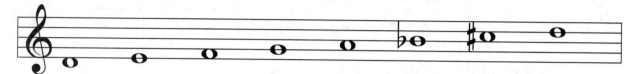

D HARMONIC MINOR SCALE

1. Write these scales.

B Major

D Major

c harmonic minor

D♭ Major

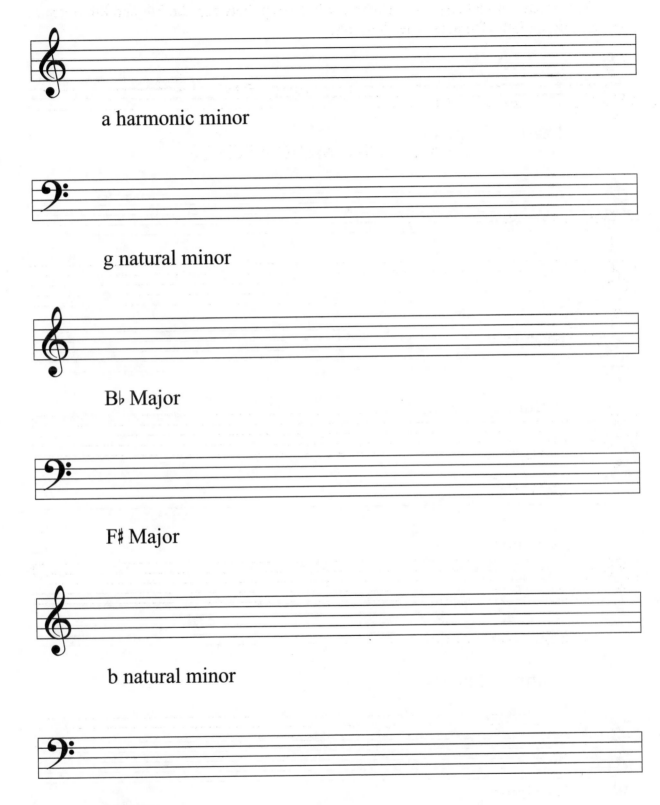

a harmonic minor

g natural minor

Bb Major

F# Major

b natural minor

E Major

d harmonic minor

Eb Major

f natural minor

Ab Major

b harmonic minor

Gb Major

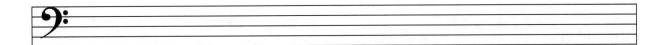

e natural minor

C♯ Major

g harmonic minor

2. Give the name and type of each circled scale in the examples below. For minor scales, be sure to put which form of minor is used. (The first one is done for you.)

a. From *Sonatina, Op. 36, No. 3*, by Clementi. ___C___ ___Major___ Scale

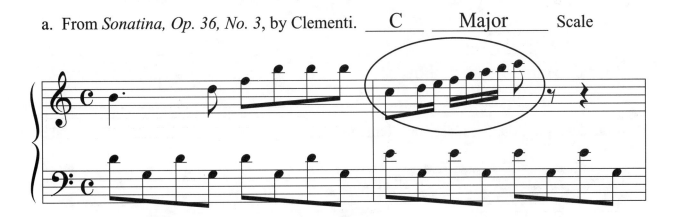

b. From *Sonatina, Op. 27, No. 11*, by Kavalevsky. _____ _____ Scale

c. From *Sonatina, Op. 27, No. 11*, by Kavalevsky. _____ _____ Scale

d. From *Variations on a Swiss Song* by Beethoven. _____ _____ Scale

e. From *Sonatina, op. 36, No. 3*, by Clementi. _____ _____ Scale

LESSON 3
THE CHROMATIC SCALE

There are scales other than Major and minor. One of these is the **Chromatic Scale**.

The **CHROMATIC SCALE** is a series of 13 notes. Each note is a half step away from its neighbor.

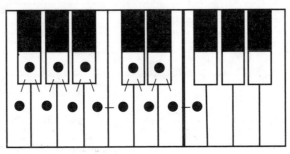

CHROMATIC SCALE BEGINNING ON F

When writing the Chromatic Scale on the staff, sharps are used when the scale is ascending, and flats are used when the scale is descending.

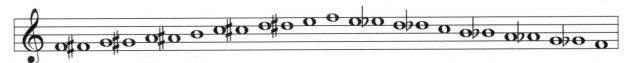

CHROMATIC SCALE BEGINNING ON F

1. Add the necessary sharps and flats to complete these chromatic scales.

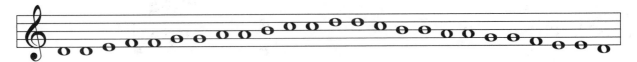

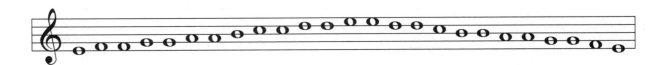

2. Write chromatic scales beginning on the pitches given, ascending and descending.

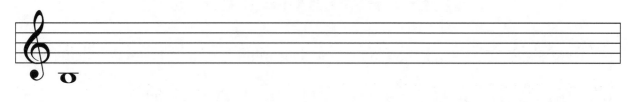

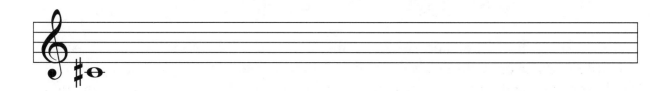

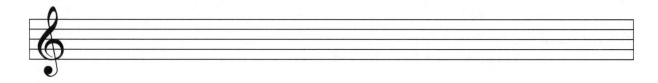

LESSON 4
INTERVALS

An **INTERVAL** is the distance between two notes. Intervals are named with numbers.

When naming intervals, count the two notes that make the interval, and all the lines and spaces, or all the letter names, between the two notes.

If the top note of the interval is within the key of the bottom note, the interval is Major or Perfect. 2nds, 3rds, 6ths, and 7ths are Major, and 4ths, 5ths, and 8ths are Perfect.

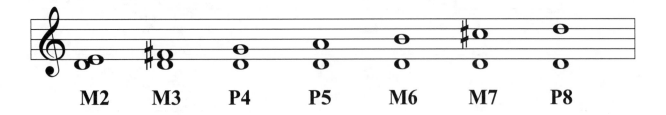

To write a Major or Perfect interval above a given note, determine the key signature for the lower note, and write any accidentals that are in the key signature before the upper note.

To write a Major or Perfect interval below a given note, determine all possibilities the note could be. Choose the key that contains the given upper note.

In the example below, a M7 below C is needed. The three possibilities are D, D♭, and D♯. The key of D♭ Major has C, D Major has C♯, and D♯ has C double sharp. The answer, therefore, is D♭.

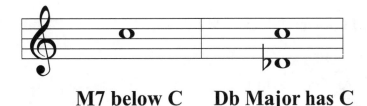

M7 below C   Db Major has C

1. Name these intervals. Give their qualities (Major or Perfect) and number names (2nd, 3rd, etc.). The first one is given.

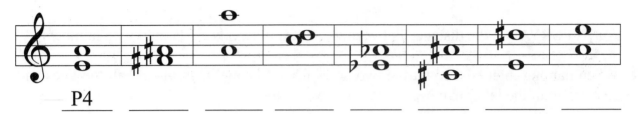

    P4

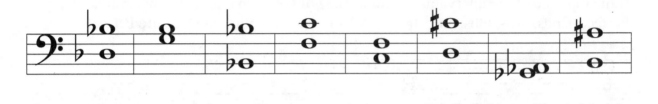

2. Complete these intervals. The first one is given.

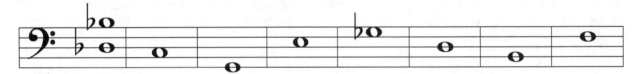

M6 up   M3 down   P5 up   P4 down   M2 down   M7 up   P8 up   M3 down

P8 up   M3 down   P4 up   M2 down   P5 up   P4 up   M6 down   M7 down

If a Major 2nd, 3rd, 6th, or 7th is made smaller by lowering the top note or raising the bottom note a half step, without changing the letter name of either note, the interval becomes minor.

M6   **m6**   **m6**   **M3**   **m3**   **m3**

3. Name these intervals. Give their qualities (Major, Perfect, or minor) and number names (2nd, 3rd, etc.). The first one is given.

m6 ___ ___ ___ ___ ___ ___ ___

___ ___ ___ ___ ___ ___ ___

4. Complete these intervals.

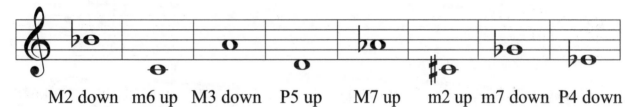

M2 down   m6 up   M3 down   P5 up   M7 up   m2 up   m7 down   P4 down

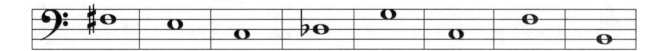

M3 up   m3 down   M2 up   P4 up   P5 down   M6 down   P4 up   P8 down

Try to bowl a perfect game with intervals and
PBJ's *Basics of Keyboard Theory Computer Activities, Levels 5-6.*
See full page ad in the front of this book.

When naming intervals within a piece of music, follow these steps:

a. Write the sharps or flats from the key signature in front of the notes. (This way, you will not forget to consider them while naming the interval.)

b. Determine the number for the interval (by counting the lines and spaces, or the letter names).

c. Using the key signature for the <u>lowest</u> note of the interval, find the quality (Major, minor, or Perfect).

5. Name the circled intervals in the passages below. Follow the steps listed above for each interval.

a. From Clementi: *Sonatina, Op. 36, No. 3.*

b. From J.S. Bach: *Short Prelude No. 5.*

c. From Beethoven: *Variations on a Swiss Song.*

LESSON 5
MAJOR, MINOR, AND DIMINISHED TRIADS

A **TRIAD** is a three note chord.

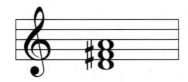

D MAJOR TRIAD

MAJOR TRIADS are made up of the first, third, and fifth notes of the Major scale with the same letter name. The lowest note of a Major triad in root position (with the notes each a third apart) names the triad.

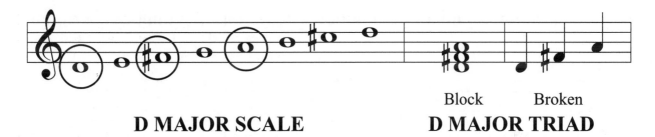

Block   Broken

D MAJOR SCALE   **D MAJOR TRIAD**

1. Write these triads. (The first one is done for you.)

E Major   Db Major   Bb Major   F# Major   Cb Major   Eb Major

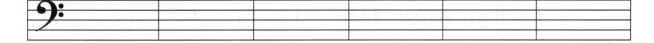

A Major   Bb Major   B Major   D Major   Gb Major   Ab Major

To change a Major triad into a **MINOR** triad, lower the middle note (the third) a half step. Minor triads have the same sharps or flats found in the minor key signature with the same letter name.

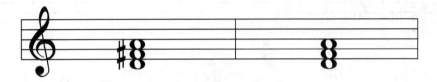

D MAJOR TRIAD   D MINOR TRIAD

2. Write these minor triads. (The first one is done for you.)

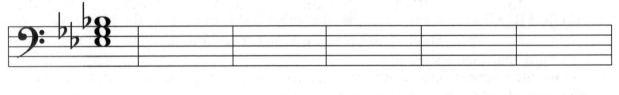

eb minor   b minor   d minor   bb minor   g minor   ab minor

gb minor   bb minor   a minor   f minor   c# minor   e minor

To change a Major triad into a **DIMINISHED** triad, lower the middle note (the third) and the top note (the fifth) a half step each. The intervals between the notes are both minor thirds.

D MAJOR TRIAD   D DIMINISHED TRIAD

3. Write these triads. (The first one is done for you. "dim." stands for "diminished.")

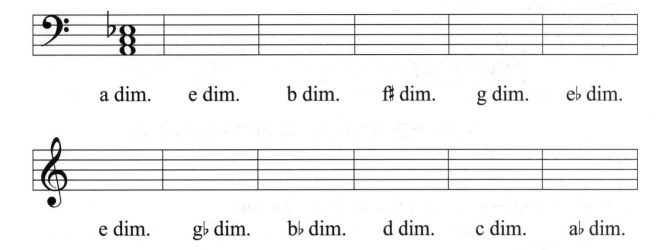

a dim.　　e dim.　　b dim.　　f♯ dim.　　g dim.　　e♭ dim.

e dim.　　g♭ dim.　　b♭ dim.　　d dim.　　c dim.　　a♭ dim.

4. Name these triads with their letter names (roots) and qualities (Major, minor, or diminished). (The first one is done for you.)

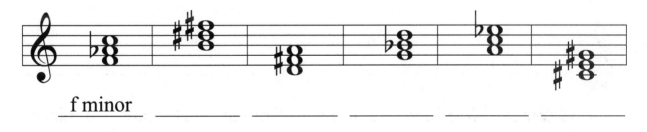

f minor　　_____　　_____　　_____　　_____　　_____

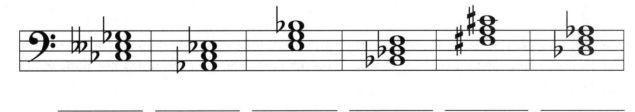

_____　　_____　　_____　　_____　　_____　　_____

5. Write these triads.

Ab Major   d minor   E Major d diminished f minor Eb Major

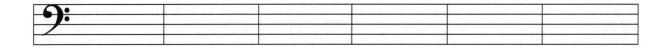

G Major   A Major   eb minor c# diminished F# Major e minor

LESSON 6
INVERSIONS OF TRIADS

A **ROOT POSITION TRIAD** occurs when the note which names the triad is on the bottom. Root position triads are called 5/3 triads, because when the triad is in its simplest position, the intervals from the bottom note are a 5th and a 3rd. When labelling a triad in root position, only the letter name and quality are needed.

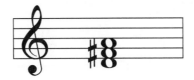

D Major Root Position Triad

A **FIRST INVERSION TRIAD** occurs when the **third** or **middle** note of the triad is on the bottom. First inversion triads are called 6/3 triads, because when they are in their simplest position (with the notes close together), they contain the intervals of a 6th and a 3rd above the bottom note. In this simple position, **the top note of the triad gives it its name.**

When labelling first inversion triads, the symbol "6" is used beside the name of the triad.

D Major Root Position Triad   D Major First Inversion Triad
(D Major 6)

A **SECOND INVERSION TRIAD** occurs when the **<u>fifth</u>** or **<u>top</u>** note of the triad is on the bottom. Second inversion triads are called 6/4 triads, because when they are in their simplest position (with the notes close together), they contain the intervals of a 6th and a 4th above the bottom note. In this simple position, **the middle note of the triad gives it its name.**

D Major	D Major	D Major
Root Position	First Inversion	Second Inversion
Triad	Triad	Triad
(D Major)	(D Major 6)	(D Major 6/4)

1. Name these triads with their roots (letter names), qualities, and inversions. (The first one is done for you.)

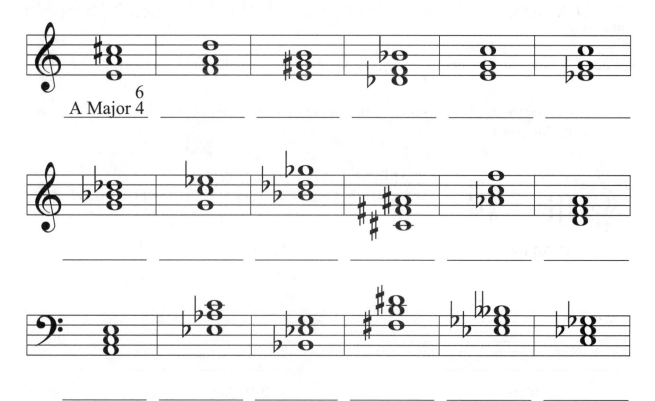

A Major 6/4

2. Write these triads.

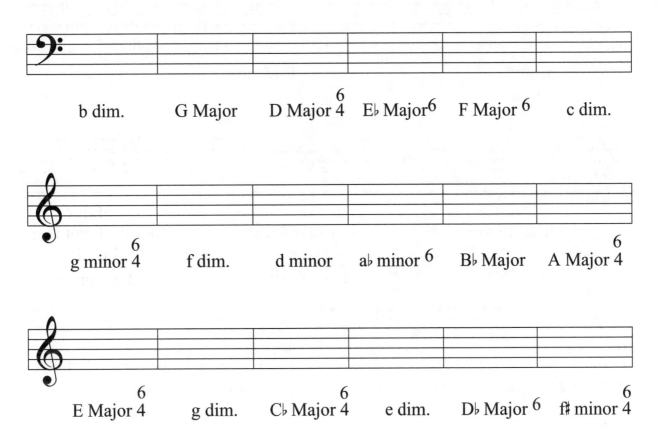

b dim.   G Major   D Major $^6_4$ E♭ Major^6 F Major ^{6} c dim.

g minor $^6_4$ f dim.   d minor   a♭ minor ^{6} B♭ Major   A Major $^6_4$

E Major $^6_4$ g dim.   C♭ Major $^6_4$ e dim.   D♭ Major ^{6} f♯ minor $^6_4$

3. Write these triads in root position, first inversion, and second inversion. (The first one is done for you.)

D Major   G Major

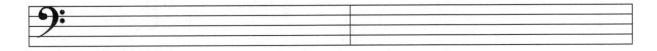

e minor   c minor

d♭ minor   F Major

E♭ Major   f♯ minor

C♯ Major   b♭ minor

A Major   b minor

g minor   e♭ minor

In actual music, triads are rarely in their simplest positions. To determine the letter name and quality of a triad within a piece, do the following:

a. Put the triad in its simplest form by placing the letter names so that there is one letter between each (for example, F-C-F-A becomes F-A-C).

b. Place all sharps or flats from the key signature, or from earlier in the measure, beside the letter names.

c. Determine the quality of the triad.

d. Determine the inversion of the triad by looking at the lowest note on the lowest staff.

Example (from *The Merry Farmer* by Schumann):

B♭ Major ⁶

a. Notes are D-F-B♭-D

b. Simplest form is: B♭-D-F

c. B♭ Major Triad

d. D is the lowest note (in the bass clef), so the triad is in first inversion (6/3)

e. B♭ Major ⁶

4. Name the circled triads in the examples below by giving their roots, qualities, and inversions. (The first triad is done for you.)

a. From *Sonatina, Op. 36, No. 3,* by Clementi.

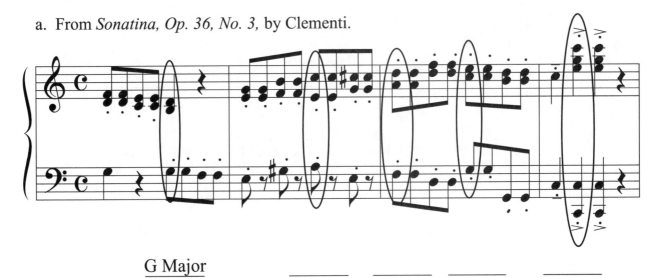

<u>G Major</u>　　_____　_____　_____　_____

b. From *Chorale* by Schumann.

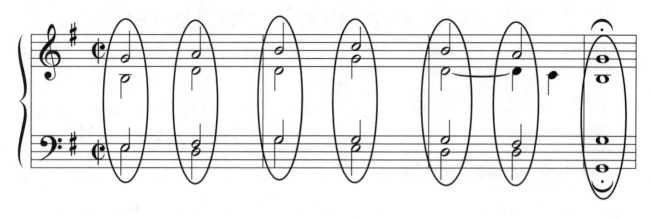

c. From *To a Wild Rose* by MacDowell.

LESSON 7
PRIMARY AND SECONDARY TRIADS

A triad can be built on each note of the scale.

Triads Built on the Notes of D Major Scale

When building triads on scale tones, all of the sharps or flats that are in the scale (or key signature) must be added to the chords which have those notes.

Example: D Major Scale has F♯ and C♯. When writing the triads of D Major, every time an F or C appears in a chord, a sharp must be added to it. (See above example.)

Triads of the scale are numbered using Roman Numerals. Upper case Roman Numerals are used for Major triads, lower case Roman Numerals are used for minor triads, upper case Roman Numerals with a "+" are used for Augmented triads, and lower case Roman Numerals with a "o" are used for diminished triads.

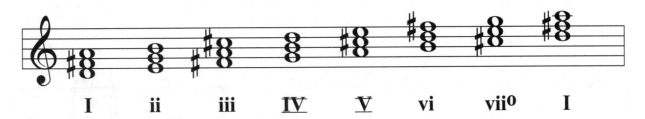

I   ii   iii   <u>IV</u>   <u>V</u>   vi   viiº   I

<u>**I, IV, and V**</u> are the <u>**PRIMARY TRIADS**</u>. In Major keys, these three triads are Major, and are the most commonly used chords for harmonizing tonal melodies. The chords are labelled with upper case Roman Numerals.

<u>**ii, iii, vi, and viiº**</u> are the <u>**SECONDARY TRIADS**</u>. In Major keys, ii, iii, and vi are minor, and viiº is diminished. The chords are labelled with lower case Roman Numerals, and the viiº chord has a small circle beside the Roman Numeral.

The qualities of the triads in minor keys are different from those for Major keys. When using **harmonic minor**, the triads have the following qualities:

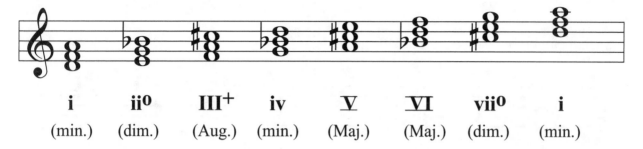

i	ii⁰	III⁺	iv	V	VI	vii⁰	i
(min.)	(dim.)	(Aug.)	(min.)	(Maj.)	(Maj.)	(dim.)	(min.)

PRIMARY AND SECONDARY TRIADS IN THE KEY OF D MINOR

i   is minor

ii⁰   is diminished

III⁺ is Augmented

iv   is minor

V   is Major

VI   is Major

vii⁰ is diminished

1. Write the Primary and Secondary Triads for these keys, and label the triads with Roman Numerals. Circle each Primary Triad, and put a box around each Secondary Triad. Do not use a key signature. Write the sharps or flats before the notes. (The first one is done for you.)

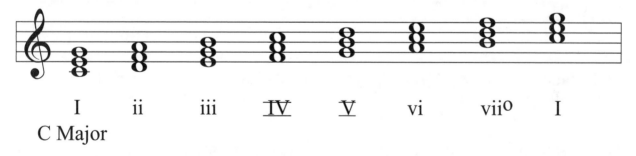

I	ii	iii	IV	V	vi	vii⁰	I

C Major

e harmonic minor

G Major

d harmonic minor

F Major

a harmonic minor

D Major

A Major

2. Write the Primary Triads for these keys, and label them with Roman Numerals. Do not use a key signature. Write the sharps or flats before the notes. (The first one is done for you.)

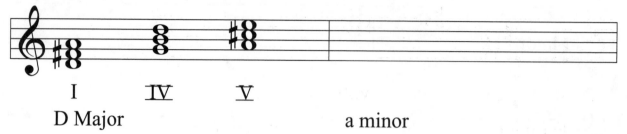

    I   IV   V

D Major   a minor

C Major   e minor

G Major   d minor

A Major   F Major

3. Write the Secondary Triads for these keys, and label them with Roman Numerals. Do not use a key signature. Write the sharps or flats before the notes. (The first one is done for you.)

ii   iii   vi   vii°

D Major   F Major

e minor   A Major

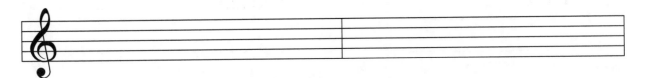

C Major   a minor

d minor   G Major

Each degree of the scale has a name. These are called the **SCALE DEGREE NAMES:**

The **I** chord is **TONIC**.

The **ii** chord is **SUPERTONIC**.

The **iii** chord is **MEDIANT**.

The **IV** chord is **SUBDOMINANT**.

The **V** chord is **DOMINANT**.

The **vi** chord is **SUBMEDIANT**.

The **vii⁰** chord is **LEADING TONE**.

(Note: Qualities used above are from Major keys. The names stay the same when in minor.)

4. Match these Roman Numerals with their scale degree names.

a. ii   _____ Submediant

b. I   _____ Dominant

c. iii   _____ Supertonic

d. vii⁰   _____ Subdominant

e. IV   _____ Leading Tone

f. vi   _____ Mediant

g. V   _____ Tonic

5. Write the scale degree names for these Roman Numerals.

I   _____

ii   _____

iii   _____

IV   _____

V   _____

vi   _____

vii⁰   _____

In actual music, chords are rarely in their simplest position. To determine the Roman Numeral of a chord within a piece, do the following:

a. Determine the Major or minor key of the piece.

b. Put the chord in its simplest form by placing the letter names so that there is one letter between each (for example, F-C-F-A becomes F-A-C).

c. Place all sharps or flats from the key signature or from earlier in the measure onto the letter names.

d. Determine the Roman Numeral of the chord by counting from the letter name of the key up to the name of the chord.

e. Determine the inversion of the chord by looking at the lowest note (on the lowest staff).

Example (From *The Merry Farmer* by Schumann):

$$IV^6$$

a. Key of F Major

b. Notes are: D-F-B♭-D

c. Simplest form is: B♭-D-F

d. B♭ Major Triad. The piece is in the key of F Major. B♭ is the fourth note of the F Major Scale; therefore, this is the IV chord.

e. The lowest note (in the bass clef) is D. The chord is in first inversion. Label the chord IV6/3, or IV^6 as an abbreviation.

6. Label the circled chords below. Put the Roman Numeral and inversion for each.
   (The first chord is done for you.)

a. From *Chorale* by Schumann. Key of _____

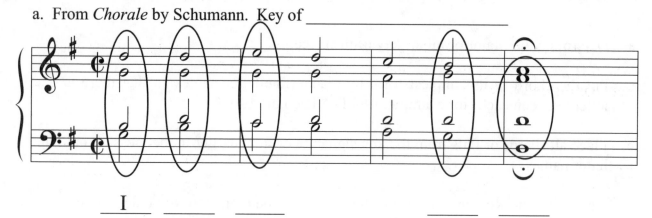

    I   ____   ____   ____ ____

b. From *Short Prelude No. 1* by J.S. Bach. Key of _____

____   ____   ____   ____

____

c. From *Little Etude* by Schumann. Key of: _____

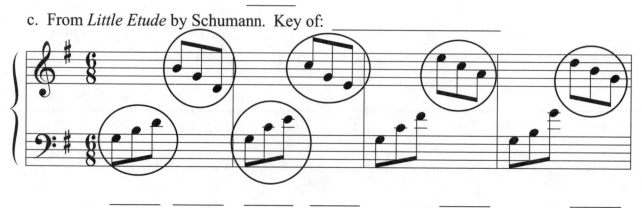

____   ____   ____ ____

LESSON 8
THE DOMINANT SEVENTH CHORD

The **DOMINANT SEVENTH CHORD** is created by adding a note to a Major triad which is a minor seventh above the root of the triad. The Dominant Seventh chord has four different notes.

D MAJOR TRIAD   **D DOMINANT
                              SEVENTH CHORD**

The Dominant Seventh is so named because it is based on the V or Dominant chord, and has the interval of a minor 7th within the chord.

To write Dominant Seventh chords within a given key, go to the fifth note of the key, and write a V chord. Then, add the note which is a minor 7th above the root of the chord. When in harmonic minor, the third of the chord (which is the leading tone or 7th note of the key) must be raised a half step.

Inversions of the Dominant Seventh chord are as follows:

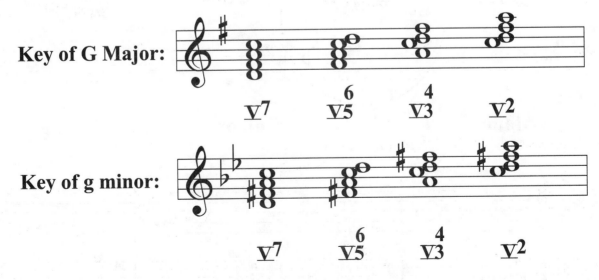

(Notice the F♯, the raised third of the chord, necessary in harmonic minor.)

1. Write Dominant Seventh chords and their inversions in the following keys, and label the chords with Roman Numerals. (The first one is done for you.)

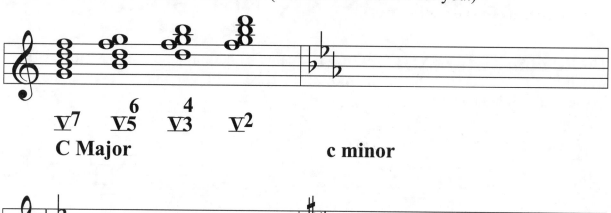

$\underline{V}^7$ $\underline{V}5^6$ $\underline{V}3^4$ $\underline{V}^2$

C Major   **c minor**

B♭ Major   **b minor**

D Major   **d minor**

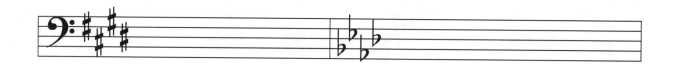

E Major   **f minor**

A♭ Major   **e minor**

2. Label the circled chords in the examples below with their Roman Numerals and inversions. Some are V chords and some are V7 chords (or their inversions). (The first chord is done for you.)

a. J.S. Bach: *Short Prelude No. 1*   b. Schumann: *Sicilienne*

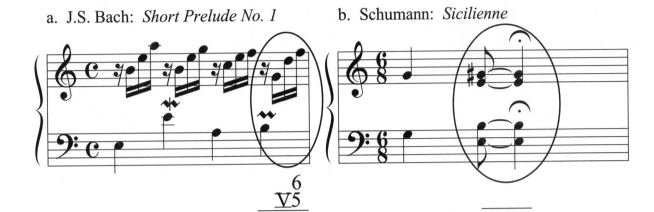

$$V^{6}_{5}$$

_____

c. J.S. Bach: *Short Prelude No. 2*   d. Schumann: *Chorale*

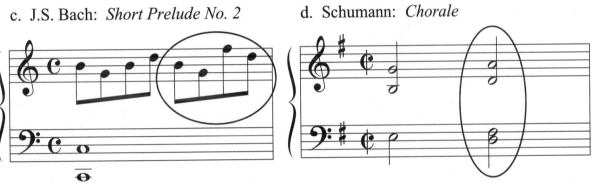

_____   _____

e. Haydn: *Allegro Scherzando*   f. Schumann: *Sicilienne*

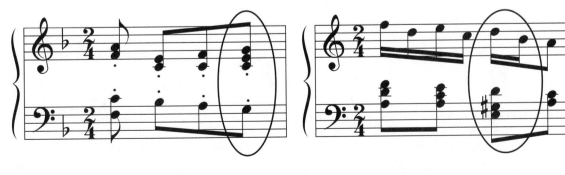

_____   _____

g. Haydn: *Allegro Scherzando*

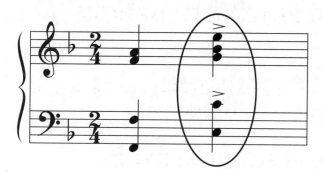

_____

h. Schumann: *Little Etude*

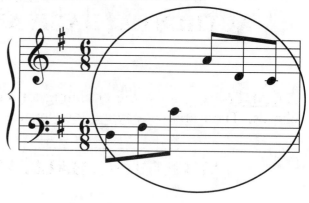

_____

LESSON 9
AUTHENTIC, HALF, AND PLAGAL CADENCES

A **CADENCE** is a closing or ending for a musical phrase, made up of a combination of chords. There are many types of cadences. Three common cadences are:

AUTHENTIC, HALF, AND PLAGAL CADENCES

An **AUTHENTIC CADENCE** consists of a V or V^7 chord followed by a I chord:

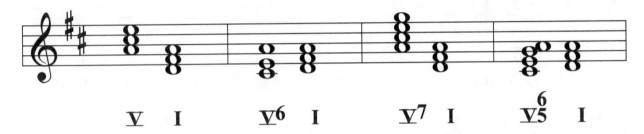

1. Write Authentic Cadences in these keys, using the chords indicated by the Roman Numerals. (The first one is done for you.) Be sure to use harmonic minor.

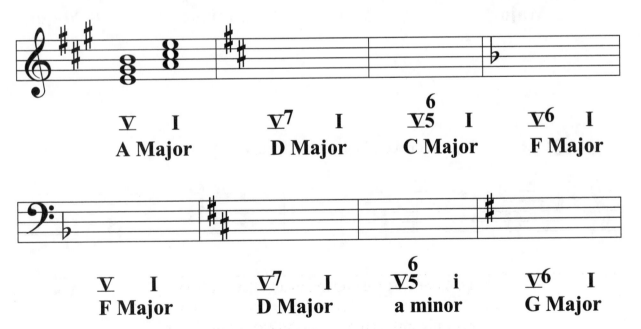

A **PLAGAL CADENCE** consists of a IV chord followed by a I chord:

2. Write Plagal Cadences in these keys, using the chords indicated by the Roman Numerals. (The first one is done for you.)

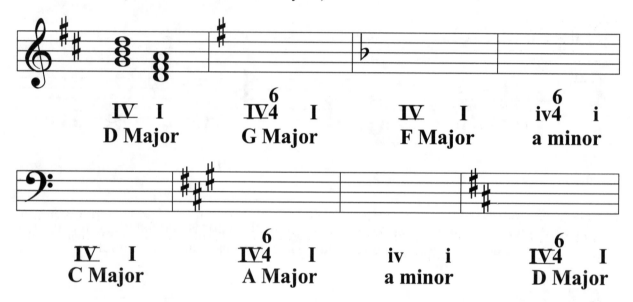

A **HALF CADENCE** is a cadence which ends with a V or V⁷ chord:

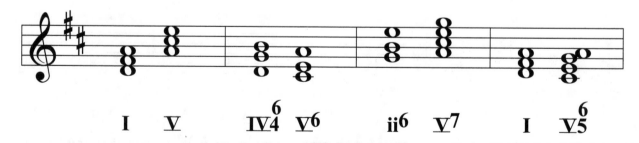

3. Write Half Cadences in these keys, using the chords indicated by the Roman Numerals. (The first one is done for you.) Be sure to use harmonic minor.

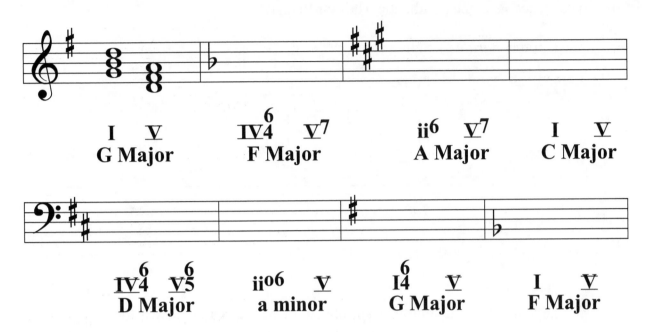

4. Label the chords of each of these cadences with Roman Numerals and inversion numbers, then put the name of the type of cadence (Authentic, Half, or Plagal) on the line below the Roman Numerals. (The first one is done for you.)

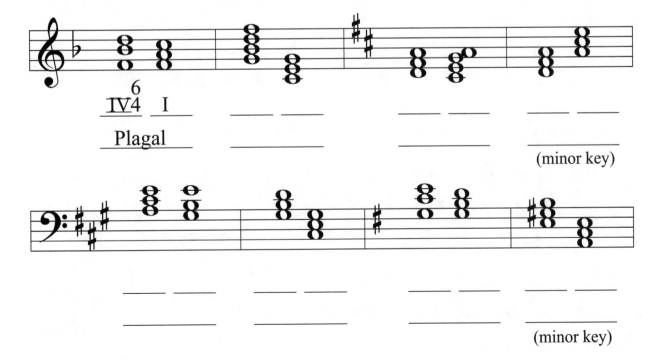

When labelling cadences in music literature, label the last two chords of the phrase with their Roman Numerals. These are the two chords which make up the cadence. Then, give the cadence its name (Authentic, Half, or Plagal).

Example (From *Chorale* by Schumann):

Key of: __G Major__   I   V

Type of Cadence: __Half__

5. Name the cadence at the end of each phrase of music below. Give the name of the Major or minor key, write the Roman Numerals for the last two chords, then write the type of cadence (Authentic, Half, or Plagal).

a. From *Allegro Scherzando* by Haydn.

Key of: _____   ___ ___

Type of Cadence: _____

b. From *Sonatina, Op. 36, No. 3*, by Clementi.

Key of: _____

Type of Cadence: _____   ___ ___

c. From *Viennese Sonatina No. 1* by Mozart.

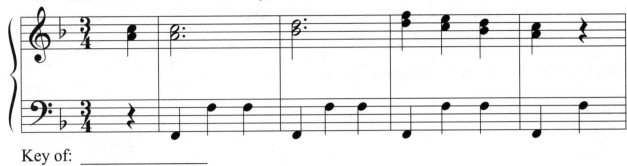

Key of: _____

Type of Cadence: _____   ____ ____

d. From *Sonatina, Op. 36, No 3* by Clementi.

Key of: _____

Type of Cadence: _____   ____ ____

e. From *Bagatelle, Op. 119, No. 5* by Beethoven.

Key of: _____

Type of Cadence: _____   ____   ____

f. From *Sonatina, Op. 36, No. 3,* by Clementi.

Key of: _____

Type of Cadence: _____

g. From *Children's Piece, Op. 72, No. 1,* by Mendelssohn.

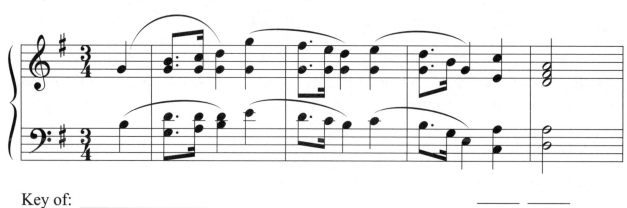

Key of: _____

Type of Cadence: _____

REVIEW
WORDS USED IN LESSONS 1-9

Authentic Cadence: A V-I cadence.

Cadence: A closing or ending for a phrase of music, made up of two or more chords.

Dominant Seventh: A Major triad with an added minor 7th (above the root).   Root position is V^7, first inversion is V 6/5, second inversion is V 4/3, and third inversion is V^2.

First Inversion: A triad written with the third as the lowest note.

Half Cadence: A cadence which ends with the V chord.

Interval: The distance between two notes, named with numbers.

Inversion: A triad written in a position in which the note that names the triad is not the lowest.

Key Signature: The sharps or flats at the beginning of a piece of music. (There are Major and minor key signatures.)

Plagal Cadence: A IV-I cadence.

Primary Triads: The I, IV, and V chords. (In minor, i, iv, and V.)

Root Position: A traid written in a position so that the note which names it is the lowest.

Scale: Eight (8) notes in order (for example, C-D-E-F-G-A-B-C). Scales need the sharps or flats from the key signature with the same letter name.

Scale Degree Names: Tonic (I), Supertonic (ii), Mediant (iii), Subdominant (IV), Dominant (V), Submediant (vi), Leading Tone (vii^o).

Second Inversion: A triad written with the fifth as the lowest note.

Secondary Triads: the ii, iii, vi, and vii^o chords. (In minor, ii^o, III^+, VI, and vii^o).

This page has purposely been left blank.

REVIEW
LESSONS 1-9

1. Name these Major keys.

_____ _____ _____ _____ _____ _____ _____

2. Name these <u>minor</u> keys.

_____ _____ _____ _____ _____ _____ _____

3. Write the key signatures for these keys, in both clefs.

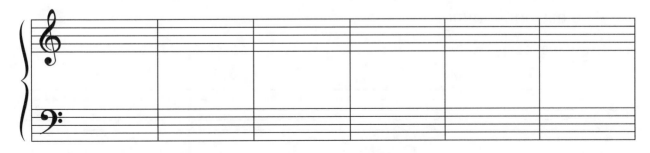

F# Major   G♭ Major   c minor   f minor   D♭ Major   e minor

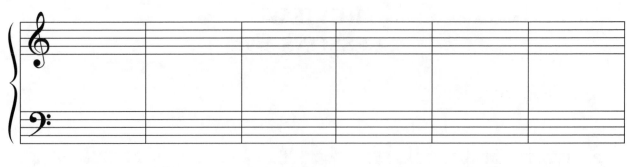

b minor   B Major   D♭ Major   d minor   g minor   a minor

4. Write these scales.

D Major

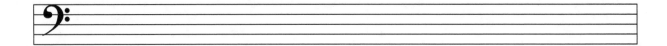

b natural minor

e harmonic minor

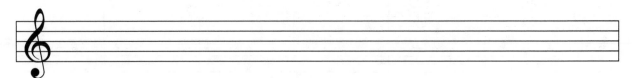

B Major

f harmonic minor

c natural minor

A♭ Major

F Major

5. Label these triads with their letter names, qualities (Major, minor, or diminished), and inversions. (The first one is done for you.)

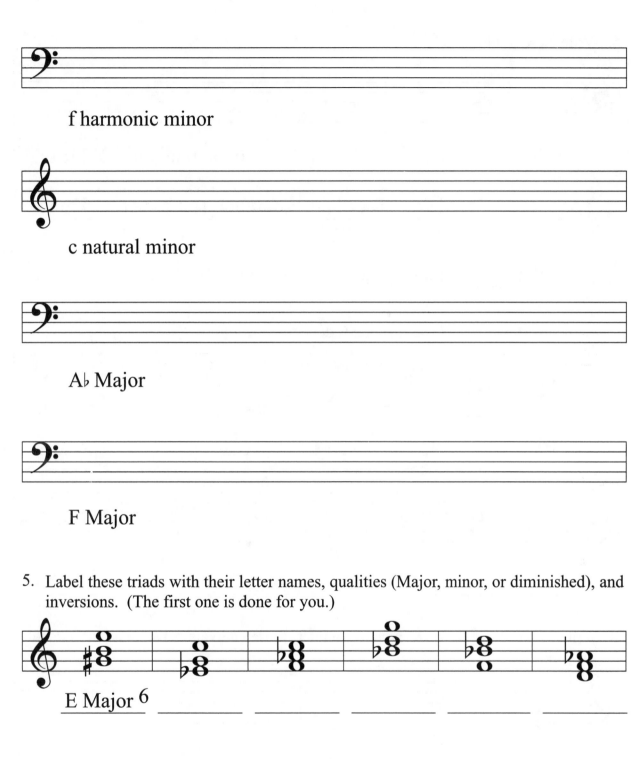

E Major 6 ___ ___ ___ ___ ___

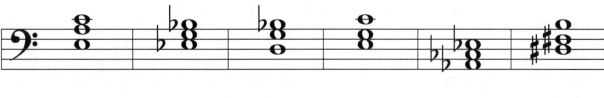

___ ___ ___ ___ ___ ___

6. Write these triads.

c dim.   E♭ Major⁶   F Major   d minor ⁶₄   b minor⁶   F Major ⁶₄

d dim.   b♭ minor ⁶₄   g dim.   A♭ Major⁶   a dim.   E Major⁶

7. Name these intervals. (The first one is done for you.)

P4 _____ _____ _____ _____ _____ _____ _____

_____ _____ _____ _____ _____ _____ _____

8. Write a note above the given note to complete these intervals. (The first one is done for you.)

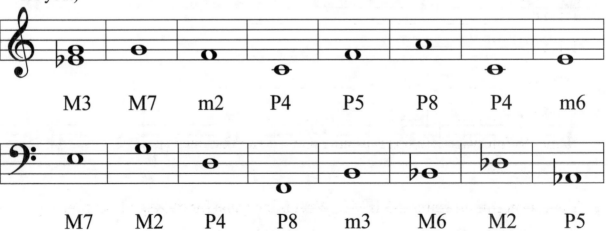

M3   M7   m2   P4   P5   P8   P4   m6

M7   M2   P4   P8   m3   M6   M2   P5

9. The following example is from *Variations on a Swiss Song* by Beethoven. Answer the questions about the music.

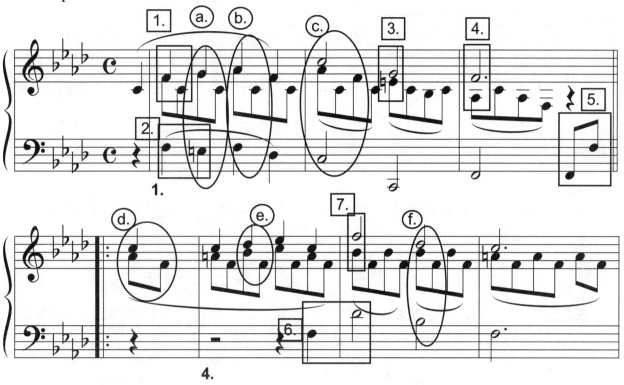

a. What is the key or tonality? _____ _____

b. Which form of minor is used? _____

c. Give the letter name, quality, and inversion for each circled chord. (The first one is done for you.)

	LETTER	QUALITY	INVERSION
Triad a.	C	Major	6/3 (First)
Triad b.	_____	_____	_____
Triad c.	_____	_____	_____
Triad d.	_____	_____	_____
Triad e.	_____	_____	_____
Triad f.	_____	_____	_____

d. Name the intervals with boxes around them. (The first one is done for you.)

   1. __P4__ 2. _____ 3. _____ 4. _____ 5. _____ 6. _____ 7. _____

e. The cadence in measures 2-3 is V-I. What is the name for this type of cadence?

   _____

10. The following example is from *Reaper's Song* by Schumann. Answer the questions about the music.

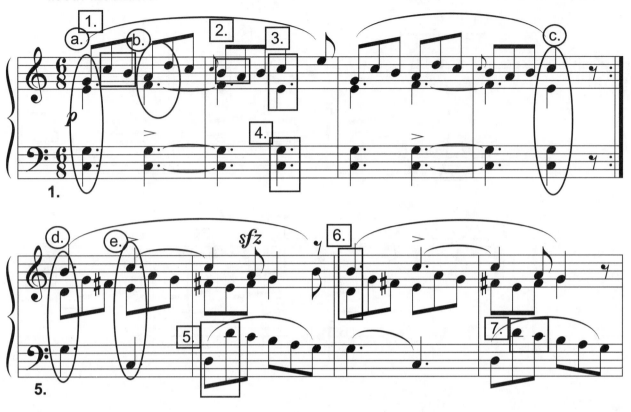

a. What is the key or tonality? _____ _____

b. What is the key in measures 5-8? _____ _____

c. Give the letter name, quality, Roman Numeral, and inversion of each circled chord. (The first one is done for you.)

	LETTER	QUALITY	ROMAN NUMERAL AND INVERSION
Triad a.	C	Major	I
Triad b.	_____	_____	_____
Triad c.	_____	_____	_____
Triad d.	_____	_____	_____
Triad e.	_____	_____	_____

d. Name the intervals with boxes around them.

1. _____ 2. _____ 3. _____ 4. _____ 5. _____ 6. _____ 7. _____

e. The cadence in measures 3-4 is V-I. What type of cadence is this? (Circle the answer.)

Authentic   Half   Plagal

f. Write the Primary Triads for this key on the staff below, and label the triads with Roman Numerals. (Do not use a key signature. Write the sharps or flats before the notes.)

11. Write the scale degree names for the following Roman Numerals.

a. I or i   _____

b. ii or ii^o _____

c. iii or III$^+$ _____

d. IV or iv   _____

e. V   _____

f. vi or VI   _____

g. vii^o _____

12. The following example is from *Allegro Scherzando* by Haydn. Answer the questions about the music.

a. What is the key or tonality? _____ _____

b. Give the letter name, quality, Roman Numeral, and inversion for each circled chord.

	LETTER	QUALITY	ROMAN NUMERAL AND INVERSION
Triad a.	_____	_____	_____
Triad b.	_____	_____	_____
Triad c.	_____	_____	_____
Triad d.	_____	_____	_____
Triad e.	_____	_____	_____
Triad f.	_____	_____	_____

c. Name the intervals with boxes around them.

1. _____ 2. _____ 3. _____ 4. _____ 5. _____ 6. _____ 7. _____

d. What type of cadence is used in measures 7-8?

e. Write the secondary triads for this key and label the triads with Roman Numerals.

LESSON 10
TIME SIGNATURES

The **TIME SIGNATURE** for a piece of music is found at the beginning, next to the key signature. The time signature is made up of two numbers:

Sometimes, the letter 𝕮 or 𝕮̸ is used instead of numbers.

𝕮 stands for 4/4, or **Common Time.**

𝕮̸ stands for 2/2, or **Alla Breve.**

The **top** number of the time signature tells **how many beats or counts each measure contains.**

The **bottom** number tells **which type of note receives one beat or count.**

2 = 2 beats or counts per measure
4 = Quarter note (♩) receives one beat

3 = 3 beats or counts per measure
8 = Eighth note (♪) receives one beat

METER is the number of equal beats per measure.

When the bottom number of a time signature is a "4," a quarter note (♩) receives one beat or count. The following chart shows how many beats to give these notes or rests:

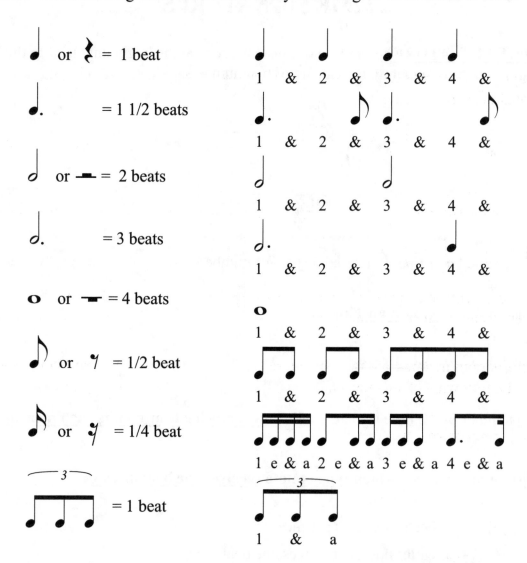

An **UPBEAT** occurs when an incomplete measure begins the piece. The last beat or beats are "borrowed" from the final measure of the piece and placed at the beginning. The counts used for the upbeat measure will be the last numbers of the time signature. The final measure will have fewer beats than normal. The first full measure begins with count number 1.

Example:

When a piece of music is in $\frac{2}{4}$ the first beat of each measure is strongest, and there are two equal beats per measure.

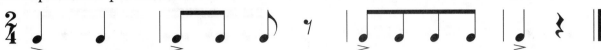

When a piece of music is in $\frac{3}{4}$ the first beat of each measure is strongest, and there are three equal beats per measure.

When a piece of music is in $\frac{4}{4}$ the first beat of each measure is strongest, and the third beat of each measure is emphasized slightly. There are four equal beats per measure.

Note: The accents above are only intended to demonstrate strong and weak beats within the given meter. They are not meant to indicate that every strong beat receives an accent.

When the bottom number of a time signature is a "2," a half note (♩) receives one beat or count. The following chart shows how many beats to give these notes or rests:

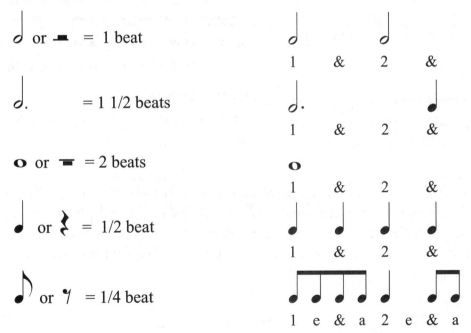

When a piece of music is in $\frac{2}{2}$, the first beat of each measure is strongest.

When the time signature for a piece of music has an 8 on the bottom, an eighth note (♪) receives one beat.

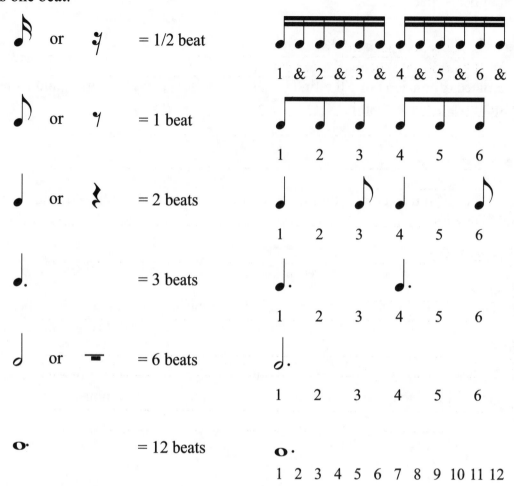

6/8 is the most common time signature which uses an eighth note as one beat. When a piece of music is in 6/8, the first beat of each measure is emphasized, and the fourth beat receives a slight emphasis.

1. Fill in the blanks. (The first one is done for you.)

2 = 2 beats per measure
4 = Quarter note receives one beat

3 = _____
4 = _____

3 = _____
8 = _____

C stands for _____

¢ stands for _____

2 = _____
2 = _____

7 = _____
4 = _____

6 = _____
8 = _____

2. Write the counts for these phrases, and place accents on the strong beats. Write the number of equal beats per measure on the line above the music. The first measure is given.

a. From *Allegro Scherzando* by Haydn. _____ equal beats per measure.

b. From *Chorale* by Schumann. _____ equal beats per measure.

c. From *Reaper's Song* by Schumann. _____ equal beats per measure.

d. From *Sonatina, Op. 36, No. 3*, by Clementi. _____ equal beats per measure

e. From *Batgatelle* by Beethoven. _____ equal beats per measure.

f. From *Fun at Home* by Khachaturian. _____ equal beats per measure.

g. From *Stars Shine Brightly* by Bartok. _____ equal beats per measure.

h. From *Prelude, Op. 11, No. 4*, by Scriabin. _____ equal beats per measure.

3. Determine whether these phrases are in 3/4 or 6/8. The eighth notes in 3/4 measures will be divided into groups of two. The eighth notes in 6/8 measures will be divided into groups of three. Circle the correct time signature for each example.

LESSON 11
SIGNS AND TERMS

Music often contains many signs and terms other than just notes and rhythms. Memorize the ones listed below.

A Tempo: Return to the original tempo (the speed at which the music began).

 Accent: Play the note louder than the others.

Accelerando: Accelerate; gradually faster.

Adagio: Slowly.

Allegro: Fast or quick.

Allegretto: Slightly slower than Allegro; faster than Andante.

Andante: A moderate walking tempo.

Andantino: Slightly faster than Andante. (Some composers use it to mean slower than Andante.)

Animato: Animated; with spirit.

 **Appoggiatura:** Used mainly in music of the Classical Period (see Lesson 15), play the first note as half the value of the second note.

Arpeggio: A broken chord that continues in one direction for several octaves:

Cantabile: In a singing style.

Con: With.

Con Brio: With vigor or spirit (with brilliance).

Con Moto: With motion.

Crescendo: Gradually louder.

D.C. al Fine: Go back to the beginning of the piece, and play until the word *Fine*.

or ℘ₑ𝒹. ❋   **Damper Pedal**: Push the pedal located on the right of the three (or two) piano pedals.

Decrescendo or Diminuendo: Gradually softer.

Dolce: Sweetly.

Dynamics: Letters or symbols which tell how loud or soft the music should sound.

Enharmonic: Two different names for the same pitch, such as C♯ and D♭.

Espressivo: Expressively.

f   **Forte:** Loud.

ff   **Fortissimo:** Very loud.

fff   **Fortississimo:** Very, very loud.

⌢   **Fermata:** Hold the note longer than its value.

First and Second Ending: Play the piece with the first ending (under the |1.   , then repeat the piece The second time through, skip the first ending and play the second ending (under the |2.   ).

Largo: Very slowly; "large."

Legato Sign or Slur: Play smoothly, connect the notes.

Leggiero: Lightly, delicately.

Lento: Slowly.

mf   **Mezzo Forte:** Medium loud.

mp   **Mezzo Piano:** Medium soft.

Moderato: A moderate or medium tempo.

Molto: Much, very.

Mordent: An ornament in which the written note is played, followed by the note below the written note and the written note again. (See example below.)

Octave Sign: Play the notes an octave higher (or lower if under the notes) than where they are written.

Ostinato: A repeated note or figure, such as:

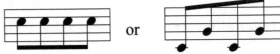

or

Parallel Major and minor: Major and minor keys with the same letter names (such as C Major and c minor).

p　**Piano:** Soft.

pp　**Pianissimo:** Very soft.

ppp　**Pianississimo:** Very, very soft.

Phrase: A musical sentence, often four measures long.

Poco: Little.

Presto: Very fast.

Rallentando: Gradually slower.

Repeat Sign: Repeat the previous section of music. Go back to the nearest repeat signs, or to the beginning of the piece if there are none.

Ritardando (*ritard., rit.*): Slow down gradually.

sfz or *sf*　**Sforzando:** A sudden, sharp accent.

Slur: Connect the first note to the second, then release the second note.

Spiritoso: Spirited; with spirit.

Staccato: Play crisply or detached.

Subito: Suddenly; at once.

Tempo: The speed at which to play the music.

 **Tenuto:** Play the note slightly louder than the others; stress the note.

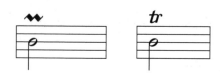 **Tie:** Hold the second note, do not repeat it.

Tranquillo: Tranquilly; peacefully; calmly.

Tre Corde: Often abbreviated T.C. in music. Release the Una Corda Pedal (left pedal).

Trill: In music of the Baroque or Classical Periods (see Lessons 14 and 15), the trill is performed beginning on the note above the written note, as in example A. In the Romantic Period (Lesson 16), the trill begins on the written note, as in example B.

A. Baroque or Classical Period   B. Romantic Period

 **Turn:** An ornament, performed as shown in the example below.

Una Corda: Often abbreviated U.C. in music. Press the left or soft pedal.

Vivace: Quick, lively.

Vivo: Brisk; lively.

-------**etto:** Word suffix meaning little.

-------**ino:** Word suffix meaning little.

1. Match these terms and symbols with their definitions.

_____ *p*

_____ *f*

_____ *mp*

_____ *sfz*

_____ *fff*

_____ *ff*

_____ Dynamics

_____ *pp*

_____ *ppp*

_____ *mf*

_____ 8*va* 8*vb*

a. Mezzo Piano: Medium soft

b. Pianissimo: Very soft

c. Piano: Soft

d. Fortissimo: Very loud

e. Mezzo Forte: Medium loud

f. Symbols that indicate loud or soft

g. Forte: Loud

h. Play the notes an octave higher (or lower) than written

i. Fortississimo: Very, very loud

j. Sforzando: A sudden, sharp accent

k. Pianississimo: Very, very soft

2. Match these terms and symbols with their definitions.

_____

_____

_____

_____

_____

_____

a. Legato: Connect the notes

b. Repeat Sign: Repeat the music

c. Slur: Connect the first note to the second note, then release the second note

d. Fermata: Hold the note longer than its value

e. First and Second Ending

f. Staccato: Detached

3. Match these terms and symbols with their definitions.

_____ ♩ (tenuto)   a. Use the damper pedal (the pedal on the right)

_____ 𝄢. ❋   b. A musical sentence, often four measures long

_____ Phrase   c. Tenuto: Stresss the note, or play it slightly louder
                                         than the others

_____ ♩ (accent)   d. Accent: Play the note louder than the others

_____ D.C. al Fine   e. Slow down gradually

_____ Ritardando (*rit.*)   f. Return to the original tempo (the speed at which the
                                         music began)

_____ A Tempo   g. Go back to the beginning and play until the word *fine*

4. Match these terms and symbols with their definitions.

_____ Allegro   a. A moderate walking tempo

_____ Andante   b. Gradually louder

_____ Moderato   c. Slow down gradually

_____ Vivace   d. Gradually softer

_____ <   e. Slowly

_____ >   f. A moderate or medium tempo

_____ Adagio   g. Quick or lively

_____ Lento   h. With brilliance

_____ Rallentando   i. Fast, quick

_____ Con Brio   j. Slowly

5. Match these terms and symbols with their definitions.

_____ Andantino

_____ Con Moto

_____ Dolce

_____

_____ Accelerando

_____ (Baroque & Classical)

_____ Una Corda

_____ Cantabile

_____ Molto

_____

_____ (Romantic)

_____

_____ Poco

_____ Tre Corde

_____ Spiritoso

a. Trill:

b. Gradually faster

c. Turn:

d. Use soft pedal (left pedal)

e. Slightly faster than Andante

f. Sweetly

g. With motion

h. With spirit

i. Little

j. Much; greatly

k. Appoggiatura:

l. Release the soft pedal (left pedal)

m. Trill:

n. In a singing style

o. Mordent:

6. Match these terms and symbols with their definitions.

_____ Presto   a. Expressively

_____ Vivo   b. A continuous broken chord

_____ Espressivo   c. Suddenly; at once

_____ Leggiero   d. Very fast

_____ Tranquillo   e. Very slowly; "large"

_____ Allegretto   f. Brisk, lively

_____ Subito   g. Slightly slower than Allegro

_____ Animato   h. Lightly; delicately

_____ Largo   i. Animated; with spirit

_____ Arpeggio   j. A repeated pattern

_____ Ostinato   k. Tranquilly; peacefully

LESSON 12
MOTIF; REPETITION, SEQUENCE, IMITATION

A **MOTIVE** is a short group of notes used in a piece of music. The composer uses this motive as the main idea of the music and repeats it in many different ways.

Beethoven's *Symphony No. 5* uses this motive:

It is repeated, with variations, several times at the beginning of the symphony:

This motive is used often throughout the symphony. It would be helpful to listen to the entire first movement of Beethoven's *Symphony No. 5*, and you will hear this motif used in many interesting ways.

REPETITION takes place when the motive is repeated immediately, exactly the way it was the first time it occurred, on the same note.

Short Prelude No. 3 by J.S. Bach uses repetition. The repetition is circled.

SEQUENCE occurs when the motive is repeated immediately, on a different note, usually a 2nd or 3rd higher or lower.

Sonatina, Op. 36, No. 3, by Clementi, uses sequence. The sequence in the example below is circled.

IMITATION occurs when the motive is repeated immediately in another voice, such as in the bass clef following a statement of the motive in the treble clef.

Short Prelude No. 4 by J.S. Bach uses imitation. The imitation is circled.

1. Circle the Repetition, Imitation, or Sequence in each example below, then write the type of technique (Repetition, Imitation, or Sequence) on the line above the music. (The first one is done for you.)

a. From *Short Prelude No. 5* by J.S. Bach.   Repetition

b. From *Courante* by Handel. _____

c. From *Sonatina, Op. 36, No. 3,* by Clementi. _____

d. From *Fun at Home* by Khachaturian. _____

e. From *Allegro Scherzando* by Haydn. _____

f. From *Sonatina, Op. 36, No. 3,* by Clementi. _____

LESSON 13
TRANSPOSITION

TRANSPOSITION occurs when a piece of music is played or written in a key that is different from the original.

For example, the first version of *Frere Jacques* below (Example A) is in the key of C Major. The second version (Example B) is in G Major. The piece has been transposed from C Major to G Major.

Notice how the intervals remain the same in both versions, and if played, the melody sounds the same, but higher in pitch.

EXAMPLE A: FRERE JACQUES in the key of C Major.

EXAMPLE B: FRERE JACQUES in the key of G Major.

Follow these steps when transposing a melody:

1. Determine the key of the original melody.

2. Determine the key signature of the key to which the music will be transposed.

3. Look at the first note of the original melody and determine its scale degree or its place in the scale. For example, if the original key is C Major and the melody begins on G, the starting note is the 5th.

4. The first note for the new key will be the same interval above the new tonic as the original. For example, when the new key is D Major and the starting note was a 5th above tonic, the new starting note will be A, a 5th above D.

5. Continue writing the transposition by determining each interval of the original melody and using that interval for the new melody. Add any necessary sharps or flats.

6. Check your progress by following steps 3 and 4 for any given note.

Example: *Mary Had a Little Lamb*, transposed from C Major to G Major.

1. Original key: C Major.

2. New key signature for G Major: F♯.

3. First note of original is E, the 3rd note of C Major

4. Starting note will be B, the 3rd note of G Major.

5. Melody moves up and down by seconds and thirds. See examples below.

MARY HAD A LITTLE LAMB in C Major

MARY HAD A LITTLE LAMB in G Major

Another way to transpose a melody is to move each note up or down the same distance. In the example of *Mary Had a Little Lamb* above, each note would be raised a Perfect 5th above the original. The first E becomes B, the D becomes A, the C becomes G, etc.

1. Determine the original key and the key to which each of these melodies has been transposed.

a. *Twinkle, Twinkle Little Star:* Original key _____

    Twinkle Twinkle Little Star: Transposed to _____

b. *Did You Ever See a Lassie:* Original key _____

    Did You Ever See a Lassie: Transposed to _____

2. Transpose these melodies to the given key. Write the transposition on the blank staff.

a. Hot Cross Buns in C Major

Transpose to G Major

b. Melody in G Major

Melody: Transpose to F Major

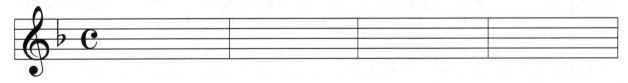

LESSON 14
THE FOUR PERIODS OF MUSIC HISTORY
THE BAROQUE PERIOD

There are four periods of music history:

> Baroque: 1600-1750
> Classical: 1750-1830
> Romantic: 1830-1900
> Contemporary: 1900-present

Music of the **BAROQUE PERIOD** (1600-1750) is characterized by the following:

a. **Polyphonic Texture:** Two or more separate voices are interchanged to create the music. The melodies are passed between the parts, and the parts are of equal importance.

b. **Use of Ornamentation:** Composers included many trills, mordents, and other ornaments in their music. It was the performer's responsibility to know how to play the ornaments correctly. Performers could also add their own ornaments at appropriate places in the music.

c. **Improvisation:** Not only did music of the Baroque Period contain many ornaments, the performer was also free to improvise sections of the music. This not only included adding the ormanents mentioned above, but also playing **cadenzas,** an entire section of music that the performer created, often after a cadence in the music.

Another type of imporvisation in Baroque music was the use of **Figured Bass.** From an outline of the chord progression of a composition, the performer improvised, using the harmonies specified by the figured bass.

(Play: I   V   vi   iii   IV   I   IV   ii6   I6/4   V7   I)

d. Most keyboard music of the Baroque Period was written for the **harpsichord, clavichord,** and **organ.** The piano was not invented and perfected until late in the Baroque Period.

e. **Terraced Dynamics:** Since much of the keyboard music from the Baroque Period was written for the harpsichord, which does not have the capability of making crescendos or diminuendos, performers used terraced dynamics. This takes place when the dynamics increase or decrease by sections: *p   mp   mf   f*, rather than gradually. (This type of dynamic contrast is most prevelant in keyboard music of the period. Other instruments, such as the violin, did create true crescendos and decrescendos during the Baroque Period.)

This example, from *Short Prelude No. 5* by J.S. Bach, shows these characteristics: polyphonic texture, terraced dynamics, and ornamentation.

Four well known Baroque composers are:

J.S. Bach: Born in Germany

G.F. Handel: Born in Germany

Domenico Scarlatti: Born in Italy

Henry Purcell: Born in England

Answer these questions.

1. Most keyboard music of the Baroque Period was written for which three instruments?

    _____

2. Describe two types of improvisation used in Baroque music.

    _____

    _____

3. What type of ornamentation was used in Baroque music?

    _____

    _____

4. What texture is common in music of the Baroque Period?

    _____

5. Why were terraced dynamics used in Baroque music?

    _____

6. Name four Baroque composers and their birthplaces.

    _____

    _____

    _____

    _____

This page has purposely been left blank

LESSON 15
THE CLASSICAL PERIOD

The Classical Period of music took place from approximately 1750-1830. Music from the Classical Period includes the following characteristics:

a. **Homophonic Texture:** Much of the music of the Classical Period has an obvious melody.

b. **Harmonic structure easily recognizable:** Quite often, the harmony of a piece from the Classical period is easy to hear, uncluttered by extra notes.

c. **Rests:** Before a new theme or section is introduced, rests are often used to set off the new section.

d. **Alberti Bass:** A common type of accompnaiment for the left hand part of piano music from the Classical Period is Alberti Bass, a repeated pattern in this style:

e. **Sonata and Sonatina forms:** A sonata or sonatina may contain several movements (usually 2, 3, or 4), with the first movement having an Exposition, Development, and Recapitulation. When there are three movements, the second is usually a slow movement in a different but related key, and the third is often a Rondo (ABACABA form), in the same key as the first movement.

This example, from *Sonatina, Op. 36, No. 3* by Clementi, shows these characteristics: Homophonic texture, clear melody and harmony, use of rests.

Four well known composers from the Classical Period are:

Franz Josef Haydn: Born in Austria

Wolfgang Amadeus Mozart: Born in Austria

Muzio Clementi: Born in Italy

Ludwig van Beethoven: Born in Germany

Answer these questions.

1. What musical form was developed during the Classical Period?

   _____

2. What type of texture is common in music of the Classical Period?

   _____

3. Name the repeated bass pattern developed during the Classical Period.

   _____

4. What is one way that composers of the Classical Period used rests?

   _____

5. Describe the way in which melody and harmony are used in music of the Classical Period.

   _____

6. Name four composers of the Classical Period and their birthplaces.

   _____

   _____

LESSON 16
THE ROMANTIC PERIOD

The Romantic Period was from approximately 1830-1900. The Romantic Period is the most popular of the four periods of music history. Some characteristics of this music are:

a. **Music became more emotional:** Much of the music of the Romantic Period was written about things, people, places, or feelings. The titles in music of the period reflect the mood of the piece (such as *The Merry Farmer* by Schumann, *To a Wild Rose* by MacDowell, or *Elfin Dance* by Grieg.

b. **Harmonies more complicated:** Composers began to add more colorful notes to their chords, using more chromaticism, and not staying within the tonal scale as much as in music of the Classical Period.

c. **Lyric Melodies:** Many of the melodies in music of the Romantic Period are lovely, singing melodies that have become favorites among music lovers.

d. **Rhythms more complicated:** Music of the Romantic Period contains many syncopated rhythms (strong notes on weak beats), complicated sixteenth note and dotted note combinations, triplets, cross rhythms (2 against 3), etc.

This example, from *Reaper's Song* by Schumann, shows these characteristics: A descriptive title, more complex chords, more complicated rhythms (notice the ties), lyric melody.

Four well known composers of the Romantic Period are:

Franz Schubert: Born in Austria

Robert Schumann: Born in Germany

Peter Tchaikovsky: Born in Russia

Edvard Grieg: Born in Norway

Answer these questions.

1. What type of titles are often used in music of the Romantic Period?

_____

2. What changes took place in the harmonies of the music from the Romantic Period?

_____

3. What type of melodies occur in music from the Romantic Period?

_____

4. Describe some types of rhythms used in Romantic music.

_____

5. Name four composers from the Romantic Period and their birthplaces.

_____

_____

_____

LESSON 17
THE CONTEMPORARY PERIOD

Many changes have taken place in the way music sounds during the Contemporary Period (1900-present).

a. **Major and minor tonalities avoided**, with non-tonal (not in Major or minor keys) harmonies being used.

b. **Quartal Harmony:** The use of 4ths to make up chords, rather than thirds.

QUARTAL HARMONY

c. **Bitonality:** The use of two different keys at the same time.

BITONALITY

d. **Polytonality:** The use of many different keys at the same time.

POLYTONALITY

e. **Atonality:** No specific key used.

ATONALITY

f. **Irregular and changing meters:** Composers often use uncommon time signatures such as 5/4 or 7/4, or change the time signature during the course of the music.

g. **Polyphonic texture:** The harmonies in music of the Contemporary Period often are the result of the entangling of independent melodic lines.

h. **Use of Classical forms:** Composers often write Sonatas, Sonatinas, or other forms which were common during the Classical Period.

This example, from *Evening in the Country* by Bartok, shows these characteristics: Polyphonic texture, changing meter, avoidance of Major or minor tonalities.

Four well known Contemporary composers are:

Bela Bartok: Born in Hungary

Dmitri Kabalevsky: Born in Russia

Alexander Tcherepnin: Born in Russia

Serge Prokofiev: Born in Russia

Answer these questions.

1. Give the name for each of these types of tonality:

a. _____ Two separate keys played at the same time.

b. _____ 4ths used for harmonies (rather than 3rds).

c. _____ No specific key used.

d. _____ Several different keys played at the same time.

2. What has happened to Major and minor tonalities in music of the Contemporary Period?

_____

3. What types of meters are used in music of the Contemporary Period?

_____

4. What is a common texture used in music of the Contemporary Period?

_____

5. What forms are often used in this music?

_____

6. Name four composers of the Contemporary Period and their birthplaces.

_____

_____

_____

_____

REVIEW
LESSONS 10-17

1. Write the counts for each example below, and place accents on the strong beats. Write the number of equal beats per measure on the line above the music.

a. From *Sicilienne* by Schumann. _____ equal beats per measure

b. From *For Children Book 1, No. 35,* by Bartok. _____ equal beats per measure

2. Define these terms.

a. Largo _____

b. Animato _____

c. Con brio _____

d. Vivo _____

e. Con _____

f. Tranquillo _____

g. Enharmonic _____

h. Con moto _____

i. Ostinato _____

j. _____

k. _____

l. _____

3. Tell which compositional technique (Repetition, Imitation, or Sequence) is used in the circled motive for each of these examples.

a. From *Jest*, by Bartok. _____

b. From *March in E♭*, by J.S. Bach. _____

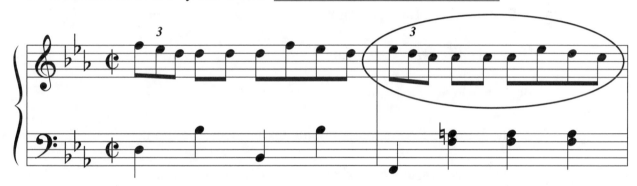

c. From *Pentatonic Tune,* by Bartok. _____

4. Name the four periods of music history and their approximate dates.

_____

_____

_____

_____

5. Tell whether these statements are true or false.

a. _____ Beethoven was a Contemporary composer.

b. _____ Bartok was American.

c. _____ J.S. Bach was a Baroque composer.

d. _____ Edvard Grieg was Norwegian.

e. _____ Kabalevsky was Russian.

f. _____ In the Baroque Period, homophonic texture was common.

g. _____ Alberti Bass was developed during the Classical Period.

h. _____ Contemporary music consists mainly of Major and minor tonalities.

i. _____ During the Romantic Period, music was colorful, with descriptive titles.

6. Transpose this melody to the key of A Major.

Score: _____   **REVIEW TEST**   Perfect Score = 77
Passing Score = 53

1. Write the names of the Major and minor keys for each of these key signatures.
   (8 points)

Key Signatures	**Major Key**	**minor key**

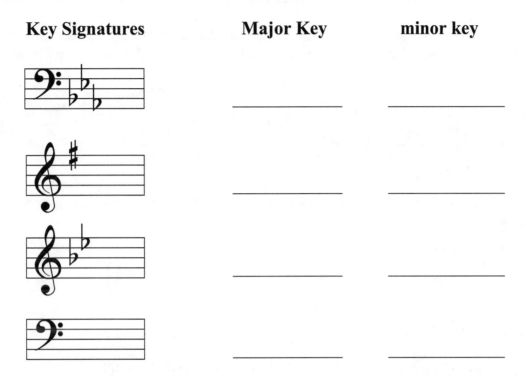

2. Write the key signature for each of the following keys. (4 points)

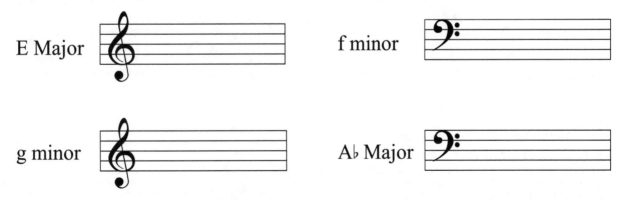

3. Add the correct accidentals needed to make B♭ Major Scale. (Do not use a key signature. Put the necessary sharps or flats before the notes.) (1 point)

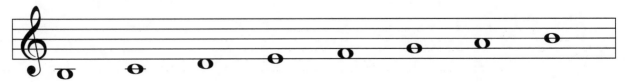

4. a. Add the correct accidentals to make c minor scale, natural form. (Do not use a key signature. Put the sharps or flats before the notes.) (1 point)

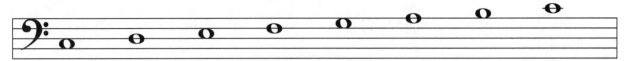

b. Add the correct accidentals to make this musical example in the key of e minor, harmonic form. (Do not use a key signature. Put the sharps or flats before the notes.) (1 point)

5. Give the letter name and quality for each of these triads. (The first one is given.) (5 points)

Ex. 1 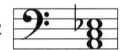 __B♭ Major__   Ex. 2 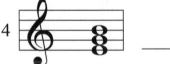 _____

Ex. 3  _____   Ex. 4  _____

Ex. 5 _____   Ex. 6  _____

6. Define the following musical terms. (8 points)

a. Animato _____   e. Con brio _____

b. Tranquillo _____   f. Con moto _____

c. Enharmonic _____   g. Largo _____

d. Vivo _____   h. Leggiero _____

7. The above example is from an Etude by Kabalevsky. Answer the questions about the music. (12 points)

a. What is the key or tonality, as indicated by the first line and the key signature?

    _____ _____

b. The music appears to be in the key of F Major in measures 4-5. Is this the relative

    Major? _____

c. Which form of the minor scale is used in measure 1, the right hand part? _____

d. Give the Roman Numeral and scale degree name of the circled triads.

    a. _____ _____   b. _____ _____

e. Write the counts for measure 2 on the music.

f. How else can the time signature be written? _____

g. Which beats will be emphasized? _____

h. Which period of music history does Kabalevsky represent? _____

i. The motive is played twice in measure 1. What is the name for this compositional

    technique? _____

8. The example above is from *Rustic Song* by Schumann. Answer these questions about the music. (10 points)

a. What is the key or tonality? _____ _____

b. Does the B♯ in measure 1 belong to this key? _____

c. Name the ornament used in measure 3 and 7. _____

d. Name the circled intervals. Give the quality and number. (The first one is given.)

   1. __M2__   2. _____   3. _____   4. _____   5. _____   6. _____

e. Which period of music history does Schumann represent? _____

f. Name another composer from this same period. _____

9. Match each of the following terms to the period of music history with which it is most closely associated. (4 points)

   a. Polyphonic texture   _____ Classical

   b. Atonality   _____ Romantic

   c. Lyric melodies   _____ Baroque

   d. Homophonic texture   _____ Contemporary

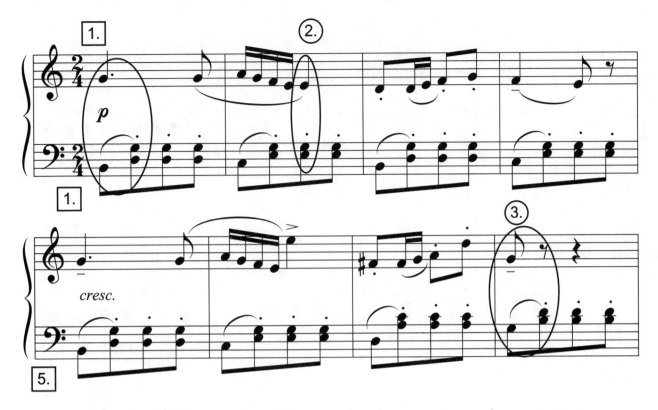

10. The above example is from *Sonatina, Op. 36, No. 3,* by Clementi. Answer these questions about the music. (15 points)

a. What is the key or tonality? _____ _____

b. What is the new key in measures 7-8? _____ _____

c. What Roman Numeral represents the new key? _____

d. Give the letter name, Roman Numeral, and inversion for each of the circled triads.

	Root	**Roman Numeral**	**Inversion**
Triad 1:	_____	_____	_____
Triad 2:	_____	_____	_____
Triad 3:	_____	_____	_____

e. What type of cadence is found in measures 3-4? _____

f. Which beats will be emphasized? _____

g. Which period of music history does Clementi represent? _____

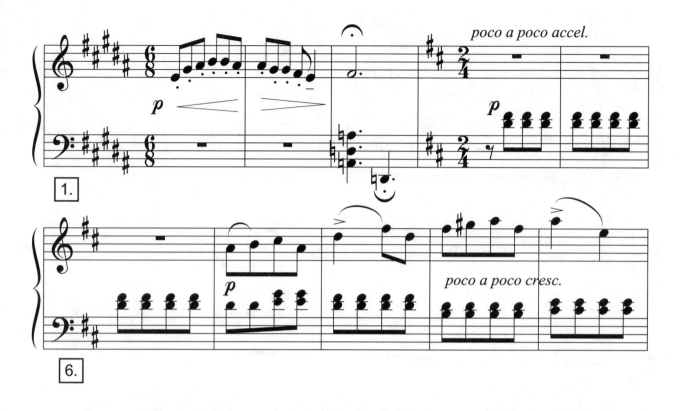

11. The above example is from *Rhapsody* by Bartok. Answer the questions about the
    music. (8 points)

a. What is the Major key or tonality at the beginning of the example? _____ _____

b. To what key does the music change in measure 4? _____ _____

c. What is the time signature at the beginning of the example? _____ Which beats

    will be emphasized? _____

d. The time signature changes in measure 4. Which beats will be emphasized in the new

    section? _____

e. Name the symbol used over the treble clef note in measure 3, and tell its meaning.

    _____ _____

f. What is the meaning of *poco a poco accel.*? _____

g. What is the meaning of the symbol ♩, used in measure 2? _____

REFERENCES

Apel, Willi. *Harvard Dictionary of Music, Second Edition.* Cambridge, Massachusetts: Belknap Press of Harvard University Press, 1972.

Arnold, Denis, ed. *The New Oxford Companion to Music, Volumes 1 and 2.* New York: Oxford University Press, 1983.

Music Teachers' Association of California. *Certificate of Merit Piano Syllabus, 1992 Edition..* San Francisco: Music Teachers' Association of California, 1992.

Music Teachers' Association of California: *Certificate of Merit Piano Syllabus, 1997 Edition.* Ontario, Canada: The Frederick Harris Music Company, Limited, 1997.

Sadie, Stanley, ed. *The New Grove Dictionary of Music and Musicians.* Washington, D.C.: Grove's Dictionaries of Music Inc., 1980.

BASICS OF KEYBOARD THEORY

Workbooks by Julie McIntosh Johnson
Computer Activities by Nancy Plourde

NAME _____

ADDRESS _____

CITY_____ STATE_____ ZIP_____

PHONE _____ E-MAIL_____

QTY	ITEM	COST	TOTAL
	PREPARATORY LEVEL	9.50	
	LEVEL 1	9.50	
	LEVEL 2	9.50	
	LEVEL 3	9.95	
	LEVEL 4	9.95	
	LEVEL 5	10.50	
	LEVEL 6	10.50	
	LEVEL 7	10.95	
	LEVEL 8	11.95	
	LEVEL 9	12.95	
	Level 10 (Advanced)	12.50	
	ANSWER BOOK	11.95	
	COMPUTER ACTIVITIES LEVELS PREP-2, Mac/PC	49.95	
	COMPUTER ACTIVITIES LEVELS 3-4, Mac/PC	39.95	
	COMPUTER ACTIVITIES LEVELS 5-6, PC Only	49.95	

Shipping:
    1-5 Books.........$5.00
    6-10 Books.......$6.00
    11 or more........$7.00

Sub-Total	
Calif. Residents: Sales Tax	
Shipping	
TOTAL	

Make checks payable to:

J. Johnson Music Publications

5062 Siesta Lane

Yorba Linda, CA 92886

714-961-0257   www.bktmusic.com   info@bktmusic.com